Composed for Joo Yeon Sir,
winner of The Arts Club Karl Jenkins Classical Music Award 2014,
in association with Classic fM

First performed on 30 October 2015 at theRoyal Albert Hall, London,
by Joo Yeon Sir (violin) and the Royal Philharmonic Orchestra,
conducted by Sir Karl Jenkins

Duration: 4 minutes

Performance materials available on hire

^{Karl}

Jenkins

Lament for the Valley
for solo violin & string orchestra
or violin & piano

Violin & piano

BOOSEY & HAWKES

Boosey & Hawkes Music Publishers Ltd
www.boosey.com

Published by Boosey & Hawkes Music Publishers Ltd
Aldwych House
71–91 Aldwych
London
WC2B 4HN

www.boosey.com

ISMN 979-0-060-13299-5
ISBN 978-1-78454-259-7

First impression 2017

Printed by Halstan:
Halstan UK, 2–10 Plantation Road, Amersham, Bucks, HP6 6HJ. United Kingdom
Halstan DE, Weißliliengasse 4, 55116 Mainz. Germany

Music origination by Jon Bunker

for Joo Yeon Sir

LAMENT FOR THE VALLEY

KARL JENKINS
(b 1944)

19628

Published by Boosey & Hawkes Music Publishers Ltd
Aldwych House
71–91 Aldwych
London
WC2B 4HN

www.boosey.com

AN IMAGEM COMPANY

ISMN 979-0-060-13299-5
ISBN 978-1-78454-259-7

First impression 2017

Printed by Halstan:
Halstan UK, 2–10 Plantation Road, Amersham, Bucks, HP6 6HJ. United Kingdom
Halstan DE, Weißliliengasse 4, 55116 Mainz. Germany

Music origination by Jon Bunker

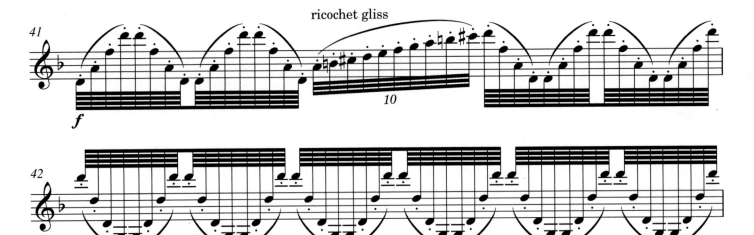

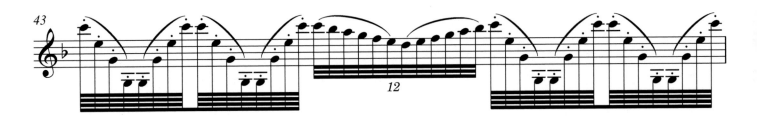

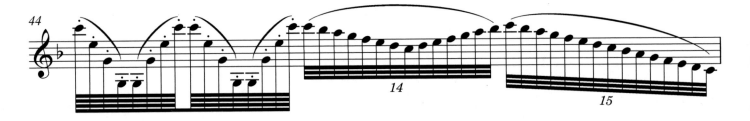

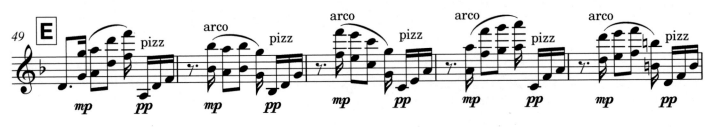

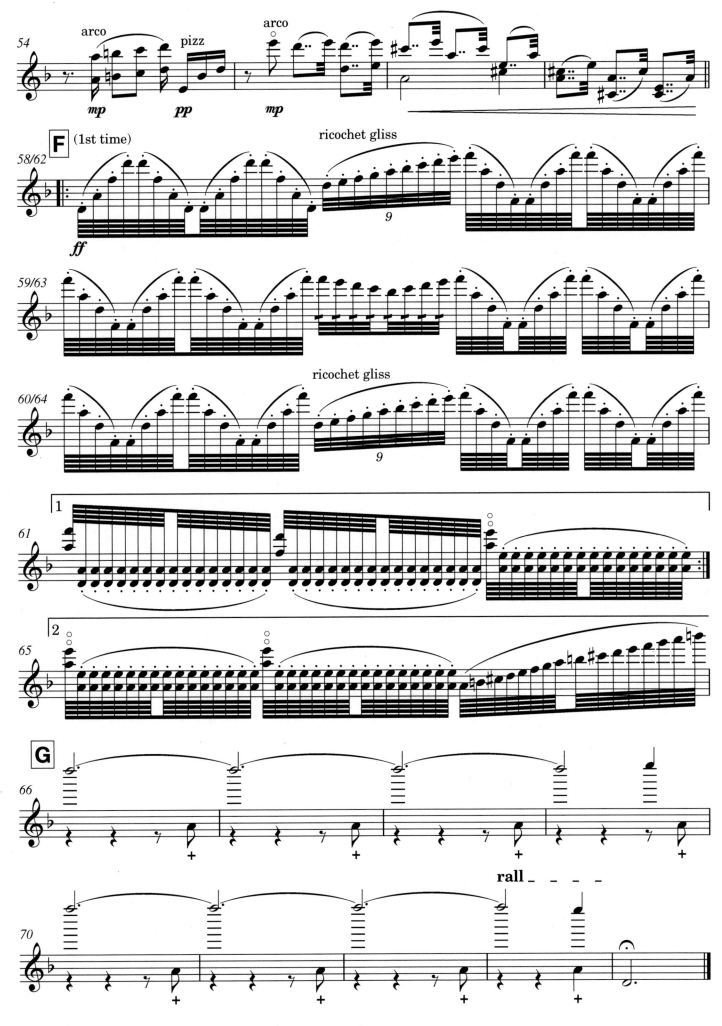

2

Solo Violin

for Joo Yeon Sir

LAMENT FOR THE VALLEY

KARL JENKINS
(b 1944)

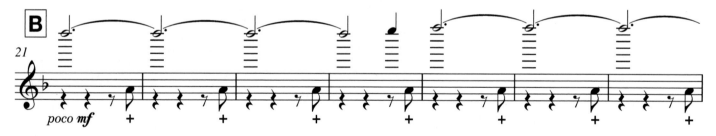

19628

Karl
Jenkins

Lament for the Valley
for solo violin & string orchestra
or violin & piano

Solo Violin

BOOSEY & HAWKES

Boosey & Hawkes Music Publishers Ltd
www.boosey.com

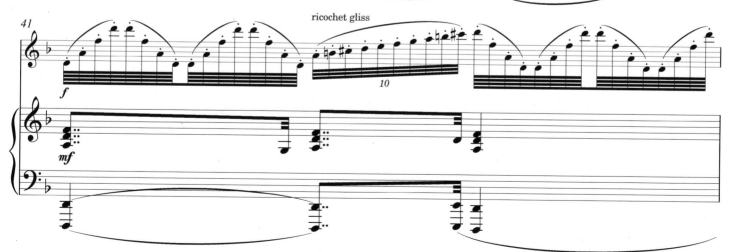

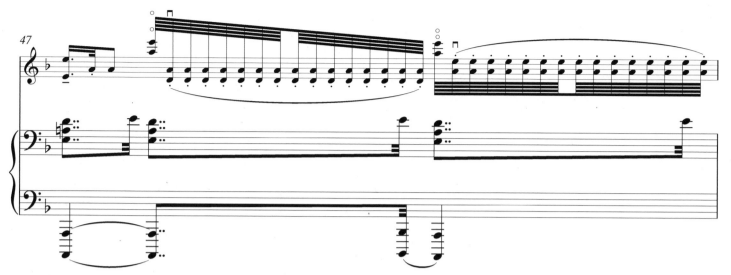

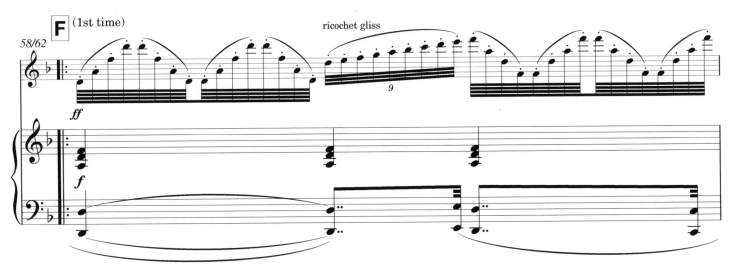

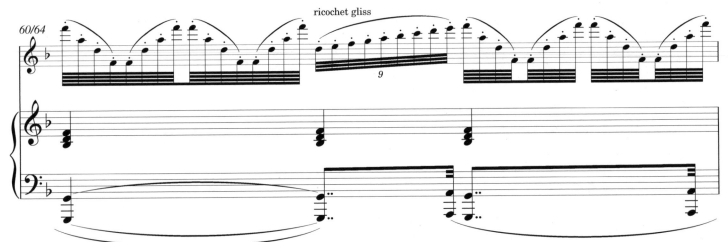

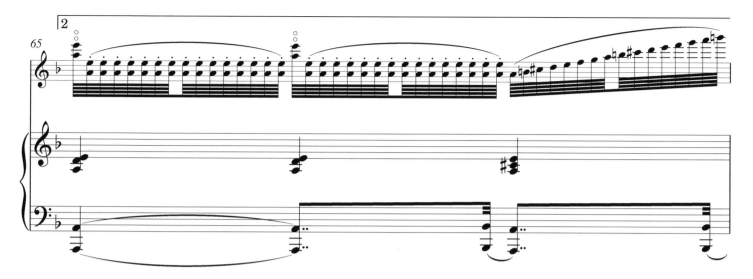